RAND McNALLY

GeoTrivia
SPORTS

Illustrated by Susan Jacoby

Rand McNally
for
Kids

CONTENTS

The Inside Scoop!

What's in the book?

What's on the pages?

MiNd BeNders

Mindbending questions—Test your knowledge, quiz your friends, and stump the grown-ups!

Answers

Correct and clever answers—Use the MINDBENDER ANSWER FLAP on the back cover to hide them. (Don't peek!)

GEO-TIP *Helpful hints— Keep these handy to help you remember what's what in sports!*

Geo-Challenge

Questions to test your sports IQ— Take the challenge if you dare!

Top Trivia

▶ *The fastest,*

▶ *strongest,*

▶ *longest,*

▶ *oldest,*

▶ *quirkiest sports trivia ever—*

▶ *Make a quest through the "-ests"!*

AMAZING FACTS

Fun and fascinating bits of information—

Amaze your friends and family with your sports knowledge!

Sports Map

Halls of Fame

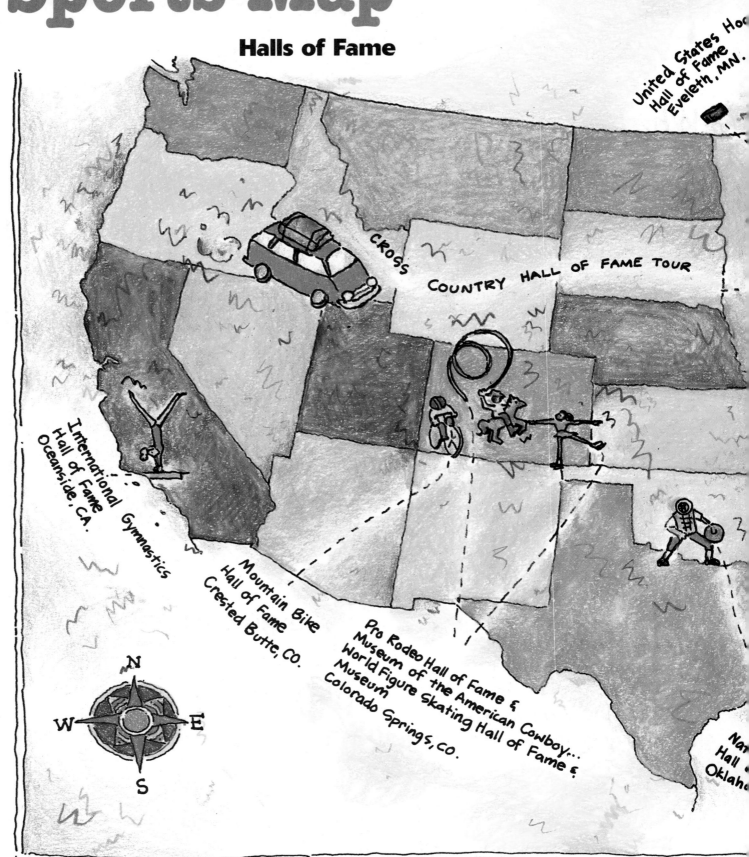

United States Hoc[key] Hall of Fame Eveleth, MN.

CROSS COUNTRY HALL OF FAME TOUR

International Gymnastics Hall of Fame Oceanside, CA.

Mountain Bike Hall of Fame Crested Butte, CO.

Pro Rodeo Hall of Fame & Museum of the American Cowboy... World Figure Skating Hall of Fame & Museum Colorado Springs, CO.

Nat[ional] Hall o[f] Oklaho[ma]

N E S W

National Ski Hall of Fame Isheming, MI.

Hockey Hall of Fame Toronto, Ontario, CANADA

Pro Football Hall of Fame Canton, OH.

National Baseball Hall of Fame & Museum Cooperstown, N.Y.

Basketball Hall of Fame Springfield, MASS.

International Boxing Hall of Fame Canastota, N.Y.

The International Tennis Hall of Fame Newport, R.I.

National Soccer Hall of Fame Oneonta, N.Y.

United States Bicycling Hall of Fame Somerville, N.J.

Lacrosse Foundation National Headquarters & Hall of Fame Baltimore, MD.

PGA/World Golf Hall of Fame Pinehurst, N.C.

Water Ski Hall of Fame Winter Haven, FL.

Indianapolis Motor Speedway Hall of Fame & Museum... National Track & Field Hall of Fame Indianapolis, IN.

International Swimming Hall of Fame Fort Lauderdale, FL.

Softball ne Y., OK.

Sports Around the World

That Wide World of Sports

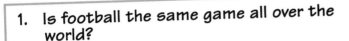

Mind Benders

1. Is football the same game all over the world?

2. True or false? The game of rugby is named after a school.

3. Is "America's national pastime" basketball, golf, or baseball?

4. True or false? In northern Europe and Russia, players on ice skates play a game called bandy.

5. If you're North American, you might hear it chirp at night, but if you're British, you might also play it. What is it?

6. True or false? In the Middle East camel racing and hunting with falcons are popular pastimes.

7. What sport began in the 1800s as an event where Mexican cowboys could show off their skills—rodeo, polo, or judo?

8. This winter sport did not start out as a sport. Is it bobsledding, figure skating, or skiing?

9. Jai-alai is a fast game played somewhat like handball. Does jai-alai mean "hard ball" or "merry festival"?

10. Is the oldest game in North America lacrosse, football, or baseball?

11. In the Scottish game of curling, are brooms used to push stones down a rink?

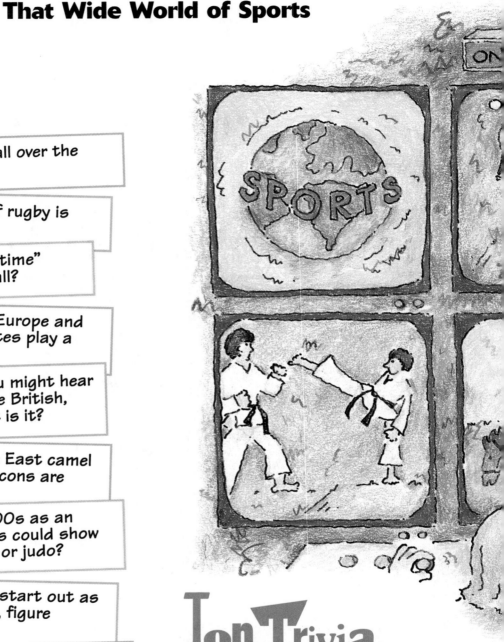

Top Trivia

▶ The world's oldest sport is probably wrestling, which originated about 5,000 years ago in the part of the world that is now Iraq.

▶ The first skier in the U.S. is believed to be a mailman who was born and raised in Norway. For 20 years, from 1850–1870, he traveled on skis carrying mail between northern California and Idaho.

▶ Taiwan is the country whose teams have won the most Little League World Series.

Answers

1. No—In most of the world, soccer and rugby are called football, and the North American game of football is called American football.

2. True—Rugby School in England to be exact, where the game was first invented. (Check out AMAZING FACTS.)

3. Baseball—"America's national pastime" is so popular it's now played on six continents!

4. True—Bandy is a game played on a rink about the size of an American football field, and it's kind of a mixture of hockey, soccer, and golf.

5. Cricket—The name of this game came from a word that meant "crooked stick," and in the early years of this game a crooked stick was used as a bat.

6. True

7. Rodeo

8. Skiing—Hundreds of years ago, people in Scandinavia fastened planks to their shoes to travel over the snow. It was a part of everyday life, not a sport.

9. "Merry festival"—Cubans gave this name to the game because it was always played at fiestas, or festivals.

10. Lacrosse—It was originally called baggataway by Native Americans in Canada.

11. No—Players can sweep the ice in front of a moving stone to clear the path so it can travel farther and faster, but a broom must never touch a stone.

AMAZING FACTS

In 1873, an English officer in Wales introduced a new outdoor game—Sphairistike. The game was a hit, but the name wasn't. That game is now called tennis.

Kite fighting is a popular sport in India, Thailand, and South America. The object of the game is to fly the highest kite. To compete, players fasten sharp objects to their kites and try to cut their opponents' kite strings.

The game of Rugby, which uses feet and hands, was invented by accident. In 1823, William Web Ellis, upset by his inability to kick the ball in a soccer game, picked up the ball and ran it across the goal line.

The Olympics
Go for the Gold

1. True or false? The Olympic Games are an international sports festival that began in ancient Egypt.

2. Which modern Olympics have been around longer—Summer or Winter?

3. Can anyone sign up to compete in the Olympics?

4. True or false? The Olympic torch is used to light the games that take place after sundown.

5. What do athletes receive when they place first, second, or third in an event?

6. Which of the following is NOT part of the Summer Olympics—baseball, boxing, biathlon, or gymnastics?

7. Which nation has won the most medals for Winter Olympic events—Norway, Bolivia, or Jamaica?

8. Nadia Comeneci was the first althlete in Olympic history to earn a perfect score of 10. Was she a cyclist, gymnast, or figure skater?

9. Was the "dream team" of the 1992 Summer Olympics the finest group of amateur basketball players ever assembled?

10. Did women's fast-pitch softball become a new Olympic sport in 1976, 1986, or 1996?

11. True or false? Olympic medals look the same every year.

Geo?-Challenge

Where will the Winter Olympics of 1998 and the Summer Olympics of 2000 be held?

(Answer on page 32.)

AMAZING FACTS

The first record of the Olympic Games dates back to 776 BC. These ancient Games took place every four years for several hundred years until they were abolished.

Solid gold? Not exactly. The first-place gold medals are made of silver and gilded with at least six grams of pure gold.

Until 1994, the Winter and Summer Olympics took place in the same year every four years. Now the Games are on a new schedule that has the Winter and Summer Olympics alternating every two years.

Answers

1. False—The Olympic Games began in ancient *Greece*. (Check out AMAZING FACTS.)

2. Summer—The first modern Olympic Games were what we now call the Summer Olympics, and they began in 1896. The Winter Olympics started in 1924.

3. No—Athletes must first compete within their own countries. Then, each country sends its own Olympic team to participate in the games.

4. False—The lighting of the torch is part of the opening ceremonies. It is lit by a flame that was started on Mount Olympus in Greece and carried by relay runners to the site of each Olympics.

5. A medal—Gold for first place, silver for second, and bronze for third.

6. Biathlon—The biathlon combines cross-country skiing and rifle shooting.

7. Norway

8. Gymnast—In 1976, Nadia not only earned a perfect score once, she did it seven times!

9. No—This U.S. team consisted of the finest *professional* basketball talent in the world, and it easily won the gold medal.

10. 1996—At the Summer Games in Atlanta, Georgia

11. False—One side always stays the same, but the other side gets a new design for each Olympics.

Superstars
May I Have Your Autograph?

1. Who broke Babe Ruth's home-run record—Hank Aaron or Cal Ripkin?

2. True or false? Muhammad Ali is the only person to ever win three world lightweight boxing championships.

3. Which one of the following skills does Jack Nicklaus use to play his sport—putting, pinch-hitting, or passing?

4. When he retired, a statue was built that read "The Best There Ever Was—The Best There Ever Will Be." But then he came back! Who is he—Michael Jordan or Magic Johnson?

5. As one of the best jockeys in the U.S., does Julie Krone ride skateboards, horses, or bicycles?

6. True or false? Pelé, one of the world's best soccer players, grew up in Brazil.

7. Walter Payton is professional football's all-time rushing leader. Does that mean he was always in a hurry?

8. Russia's Raisa Smetanina is a champion Nordic skier. Italy's Alberto Tomba is a champion Alpine skier. Which one skis faster?

9. Bill Bradley is a basketball Hall-of-Famer. Did he become a "Big 10" coach or U.S. Senator after retiring from basketball?

10. Did Canadian Bobby Orr play hockey for the Edmonton Oilers or the Boston Bruins?

Geo-Challenge

Can you match the nickname with the superstar?

1. Junior	A. Charles Barkley
2. E	B. Frank Thomas
3. Sir Charles	C. Wayne Gretzky
4. The Big Hurt	D. Jerry Rice
5. The Great One	E. Ken Griffey, Jr.
6. Flash-80	F. Emmitt Smith
7. Reign Man	G. Jack Nicklaus
8. The Golden Bear	H. Shawn Kemp

(Answers on page 32.)

1. Hammerin' Hank Aaron

2. False—He's the only person to ever win three world heavyweight boxing championships.

3. Putting—Jack Nicklaus is one of golf's superstars.

4. Michael Jordan—And that statue of Jordan is in front of the United Center, home of the Chicago Bulls.

5. Horses

6. True

7. No—Rushing in football means "running while holding the ball." (Although he might have been hurrying away from the players trying to tackle him!)

8. Alberto Tomba—Since Nordic skiers ski *across* land, and Alpine skiers ski *down* mountains, Alpine skiing is much faster.

9. U.S. Senator

10. The Boston Bruins—He also played for the Chicago Black Hawks. Orr was the first defenseman to score 100 points in a season, the first to lead the league in scoring, and the first to get more than 30 goals in a season.

Top Trivia

▶ **The biggest shoes in the NBA belong to Shaquille O'Neal. They're a size 22!**

▶ **In 1988, Steffi Graf won the Grand Slam and the Olympic Gold medal, making her the only tennis player ever to have won a "Golden Slam."**

▶ **When Mario Lemieux was 18, he scored in 61 straight games. That's a junior hockey league record!**

Fields, Courts, Rinks, & Rings

Sports Places

Mind Benders

1. Does baseball's Wrigley Field share its name with a brand of gum or cereal?

2. What's the name of the stadium where the Pittsburgh Steelers play? (GEO-HINT: It's near the Allegheny, Monongahela, and Ohio rivers.)

3. True or false? Mile-High Stadium is known for the world's tallest seats.

4. You're at Madison Square Garden. Are you watching the Knicks play basketball or the Rangers play hockey?

5. True or false? The Houston Astros have never been rained on at a home game.

6. When fans at Boston's Fenway Park speak of a "Green Monster," do they mean the green wall in left field or a talented rookie?

7. Which takes place in a rink—hockey or boxing?

8. Does the Pro Football Hall of Fame have a football or a helmet on its roof?

9. True or false? The Baseball Hall of Fame is located in Cooperstown, New York, because that's where Abner Doubleday is said to have invented baseball.

10. If you've always wanted to try your skill at Pebble Beach, is your sport golf, surfing, or tennis?

11. Is competitive tennis played on concrete, clay, or grass?

Top Trivia

▶ For home-run hitters who like a challenge, the deepest field in a U.S. ballpark is center field at Detroit's Tiger Stadium. Swing hard—the wall is 440 feet (about 133 meters) from home plate!

▶ The Rose Bowl in Pasadena and Michigan Stadium in Ann Arbor are the two largest football stadiums in the U.S., each holding more than 100,000 fans. Sound big? In the Czech Republic there is a stadium bigger than both of these put together. It holds 240,000 spectators!

AMAZING FACTS

It's so cold in Green Bay, Wisconsin, that Lambeau Field, where the Packers play, has heating coils buried below the field to melt snow and ice!

The Astrodome originally had a glass dome to let in sun and grow the grass. But there was too much glare, so an artificial turf was invented.

Answers

1. Gum—It was built in 1914 and is the oldest park in the Major Leagues. (Chew on that!)

2. Three Rivers Stadium (Baseball's Pittsburgh Pirates also play there.)

3. False—Mile-High Stadium, home of the Denver Broncos, takes its name from the city's altitude of exactly one mile above sea level.

4. Trick question, both!—The New York Knicks and Rangers call "The Garden" home, but never on the same night.

5. True—The Houston Astros and Oilers play in the Astrodome, the world's first domed stadium, built in 1962. (Talk about fair weather fans!)

6. The green wall in left field—The Green Monster is the nickname for the 37-foot-high (11.2 meters) wooden wall in left field that has frustrated home-run hitters since 1934.

7. Hockey—Boxing takes place in a ring.

8. A *giant* football—It's located in Canton, Ohio, the city where the NFL was formed in 1920.

9. True—It's located there for that reason, but the story turns out to be a myth.

10. Golf

11. Trick question—Competitive tennis is played on all three surfaces.

The Winners' Circle

The Championships

1. If you are in the Super Bowl, are you bowling or playing football?

2. True or false? Only U.S. teams play in baseball's World Series.

3. Is the Stanley Cup for thirsty hockey players to drink from?

4. In baseball, a grand slam is a four-run homer. Is there a grand slam in tennis?

5. Which of these is NOT a big college football game—the Sugar Bowl, the Gator Bowl, or the Cereal Bowl?

6. Was the first international surfing championship held in Arkansas or Hawaii?

7. Which championship is the most popular in the world—the Super Bowl, the World Series, or the World Cup?

8. True or false? The Triple Crown is the name for three races of three-year-olds.

9. If you wanted to win the America's Cup, would you practice tackling or tacking?

10. It's time for March Madness. Are you watching volleyball, basketball, or kickball?

11. True or false—The U.S. Open golf championship goes to the golfer with the highest score after playing 72 holes.

FREE!
FOOTBALL
GAME INSIDE

Top Trivia

▶ *The 1994 World Cup Final was the world's most watched television event ever! Over one billion people saw Brazil beat Italy at the Rose Bowl.*

▶ *The Tour de France bicycle race draws more spectators than any other championship. Experts guess that over ten million people watch the three-week-long race as it winds through France.*

▶ *The youngest champion athlete is Fu Mingxia from China. She won the world platform diving title in 1991 when she was only 12. And the oldest? Fred Davis won the world professional billiards title in 1980 at age 67.*

Answers

1. Playing football—This championship game has been played each year since 1967.

2. False—Both the U.S. and Canada have Major League teams that might play in the World Series.

3. Only the really good ones—The Stanley Cup is the National Hockey League's championship trophy.

4. Yes—In tennis the Grand Slam is winning four major championships: Wimbledon, the Australian Open, the French Open, and the U.S. Open.

5. The Cereal Bowl (But every football game has its share of snapping, crackling, and popping!)

6. Makaha, Hawaii, in 1963 (The surf is *never* up in Arkansas—check a map!)

7. The World Cup—Baseball and football may rule in the U.S., but worldwide, soccer is more popular.

8. True—Three-year-old horses, that is! The Kentucky Derby, the Preakness, and the Belmont Stakes make up the Triple Crown of horse racing.

9. Tacking, or sailing against the wind (America's Cup is a sailing race.)

10. Basketball

11. False—They do play 72 holes, but the golfer with the *lowest* score wins.

Rules & Regs

Stump the Ump

Mind Benders

1. True or false? The American League and the National League do not play baseball by the same rules.

2. Which one of these baseball pitches is NOT allowed—a knuckle ball, spit ball, or round house?

3. True or false? Baseball's rules say that fans who hiss or hoot at the umpire are to be removed from the grounds.

4. The referee of a football game has just raised both arms straight over his head. Is he signaling a penalty or touchdown?

5. In 1994, the NFL introduced a new scoring option. Was it the two-point conversion or the touchback?

6. Was it the NFL or NBA that added the three-point field goal in 1979?

7. After Michael Jordan returned to basketball in 1995 he was fined. Did he get in trouble for talking trash, switching numbers, or failing to make baseball's Major Leagues?

8. If you are penalized for slashing, tripping, or spearing, are you fencing or playing hockey?

9. Which is NOT allowed during play in tennis—touching the net or hitting the ball around the net?

10. True or false? Soccer players can never touch the ball with their hands.

GEO-TIP *What's a designated hitter?*

*A **DESIGNATED HITTER** is the baseball player who bats in place of the pitcher (or another chosen fielder). Only the American League has the designated hitter rule. National League pitchers must take a turn at bat.*

AMAZING FACTS

When basketball was first invented in 1891 (to keep students busy in the winter), the official hoops were peach baskets with the bottoms removed.

Golf officials change pin placement—where the holes are on the greens—to make some courses harder for important tournaments.

Answers

1. True—The American League allows designated hitters, while the National League does not.

2. Spit ball—Knucklers and round houses (curves) are allowed.

3. True (Although this rule doesn't seem to be enforced very often!)

4. Touchdown—This motion also signals a field goal or extra points after a touchdown.

5. Two-point conversion—It happens right after a touchdown.

6. NBA—Football got theirs in 1909.

7. Switching numbers—In a playoff game he suited up in his old number 23 jersey.

8. Playing hockey

9. Touching the net—The ball does not have to go over the net, as long as it lands in the opposite court.

10. False—Goalies can use their hands in their own penalty area. Other players can use their hands to put the ball back in play after it goes out of bounds.

Uniforms & Equipment

Mind Benders

1. Which of these sports is NOT played with a racket—tennis, racquetball, squash, lacrosse, or badminton?

2. You're wearing a helmet, plenty of padding, heavy tights, "shoes" with blades, and you're carrying a stick. What sport are you ready to play?

3. If you're using a mallet, are you playing pool, croquet, or table tennis?

4. Who wears leotards—gymnasts or surfers?

5. Which is NOT an item professional baseball players might wear—stirrups, mittens, or batting helmets?

6. In fencing, is the foil a light sword or mesh mask?

7. If you put on a *gi*, would you be suiting up for bowling or karate?

8. If you were an archer, would you wear a quiver around your waist or wrist?

9. True or false? Rugby is played with a ball that looks a lot like a soccer ball.

10. Can you find spikes and studs on shin guards or shoes?

11. What's a jersey? (GEO-HINT: It's got your number!)

12. True or false? Bobsleds are named after Bob, the guy who invented them.

13. Do all sports helmets look alike?

AMAZING FACTS

In the late 1950s, California surfers created the first skateboards by attaching roller-skate wheels to wooden boards. (So they could "surf" the sidewalks!)

Bull-riding is one dangerous sport! There is only one piece of equipment to help the rider stay on the bull—a rope around the bull's middle.

Geo-Challenge

Can you name the balls pictured below?

(Answers on page 32.)

Answers

1. Lacrosse is played with a crosse, which is a stick with a net.

2. Hockey

3. Croquet—Pool players use cues, and table tennis players use paddles.

4. Gymnasts—Leotards are stretchy, snug-fitting, one-piece outfits that cover the torso. (Surfers wear wetsuits.)

5. Mittens (Although most players wear mitts, which are used for catching the ball.)

6. A light sword

7. Karate—A *gi* is a cotton jacket and pants worn with a belt in a color that shows the wearer's level of expertise.

8. Your waist—A quiver holds arrows.

9. False—The ball used in rugby looks a lot like a football. (American football evolved from rugby.)

10. Shoes

11. A jersey is a type of shirt that often has a player's name and number on it.

12. False—*Bob* means "to cut short," and a bobsled is a short sled.

13. No—They are designed for each sports' particular safety needs.

Team Trivia
Nicknames, Mascots, and Colors

1. Which three Major League baseball teams were named for the color of their socks?

2. The University of Alabama's nickname is the Crimson Tide. Can you name at least one of their team colors?

3. What city's NBA team logo shows a deer with antlers—Milwaukee or Utah?

4. Which baseball team suffers the curse of the Great Bambino—the Boston Red Sox or the New York Yankees?

5. True or false? The University of Miami chose the nickname Hurricanes because they wanted their sports teams to sweep away the opponents.

6. Which of these sea-worthy names does NOT belong to a professional team—Mariners, Dolphins, Sea Horses, or Penguins?

7. Are hockey's Montreal Canadiens called the Habs or the Cabs?

8. True or false? The University of Arkansas' nickname, the Razorbacks, refers to a type of sharp knife.

9. Is the San Antonio Spurs' mascot a cowboy or a coyote?

10. Were hockey's Toronto Maple Leafs once called the Toronto Arenas or the Toronto St. Patricks?

11. True or false? Football's Cardinals were named after Arizona's state bird.

Geo-Challenge

Can you match the mascot with the team?

1. Benny	A. St. Louis Cardinals
2. Slider	B. Chicago Bulls
3. Phanatic	D. Cleveland Indians
4. BJ Birdy	E. Philadelphia Phillies
5. Fredbird	G. Toronto Blue Jays

(Answers on page 32.)

Answers

1. The Chicago White Sox, Boston Red Sox, and Cincinnati Reds (which used to be the Cincinnati Red Stockings before the name was shortened to Reds)

2. Crimson and white—Crimson is a deep shade of red.

3. Milwaukee—Home of the Bucks!

4. The Boston Red Sox—They haven't won a World Series since they traded Babe Ruth (The Great Bambino) to the Yankees in 1919.

5. True

6. Sea Horses

7. The Habs—French is the main language in Montreal, and Habs is short for *les habitants*, which means "the locals."

8. False—A razorback is a wild hog.

9. A coyote

10. Trick question, both—They originated as the Toronto Arenas in 1917 and became the Toronto St. Patricks in 1919. It wasn't until 1927 when, under new ownership, they were renamed the Toronto Maple Leafs. (Hey, shouldn't that be *Maple Leaves?*)

11. False—The team was first the Chicago Cardinals and then the St. Louis Cardinals, and they were named for the red color of their uniforms.

Top Trivia

▶ **The biggest mascot is Ralphie III—a 1,300-pound (590-kilogram) buffalo. He's the mascot for the University of Colorado football team.**

▶ **The NFL team that has retired the most uniform numbers is the Chicago Bears.**

▶ **What's the slimiest college mascot around? Probably the Banana Slugs from the University of California at Santa Cruz.**

Sports Speak
Learn the Lingo

Mind Benders

1. True or false? A sack in football is often the result of a blitz.

2. If you were bowling, would you want a turkey?

3. Is a hat trick something a hockey player or a rodeo rider would like to do?

4. In golf, would you rather get a birdie, bogie, or albatross?

5. True or false? Tackling is the same move in soccer and football.

6. In basketball, is a shot from downtown a three-point shot, a shot from out of bounds, or a shot from a fan in the grandstand?

7. Are "green monster" and "burger" terms that skateboarders or surfers use?

8. True or false? A football team with a nickel defense has a defensive line that isn't worth very much.

9. True or false? In baseball, a bolt and a frozen rope are the same thing.

10. Is a shredder a really bad skateboarder?

11. Your baseball team just swept a series. What happened?

12. Where do armchair quarterbacks play sports?

Top Trivia

▶ Of all sports, baseball is the richest source of new vocabulary. A recently published dictionary of baseball terms contains more than 5,000 entries.

▶ The riskiest play in football may be the Hail Mary, in which a pass is thrown into a crowd of players in the end zone. The quarterback knows that anyone in the end zone might catch the ball! The Hail Mary is a desperation play usually attempted only in the last few moments of a game by a team that is losing.

▶ In any sport, players who are the biggest show-offs are called hot dogs, and showing off is called hotdogging.

Answers

1. True—When defensive players blitz (rush and penetrate the offensive line), they often sack (tackle behind the line of scrimmage) the quarterback.

2. You bet!—A turkey is three strikes in a row.

3. A hockey player—A hat trick is three goals scored in one game by one player.

4. Albatross—An albatross is three strokes under par, a birdie is one stroke under par, and a bogie is one stroke over par.

5. False—In soccer, the player goes for the ball, not the person, when tackling.

6. A three-point shot

7. Surfers—Green monsters are huge waves and burgers are bumpy, uneven waves.

8. False—A nickel defense is a strategy in which an extra player is put in the backfield in addition to the usual four.

9. True—Both mean a line drive, which is also called an aspirin, BB, pea, rocket, clothesline, or seed.

10. No—A shredder is a good skater.

11. Your team won all the games in the series.

12. In front of their TVs!—Armchair quarterbacks are fans who think they can lead a team better than the players they're watching on TV.

RECORD BREAKERS

The Best of the Best

1. True or false? Lou Gehrig holds baseball's record for most consecutive games played.

2. Who holds the record for career hits—Pete Rose or Babe Ruth?

3. True or false? Larry Bird holds the NBA record for most career points (38,387).

4. Wilt Chamberlain is one of only two basketball players to have led the NBA in scoring for seven years straight. Is the other one Michael Jordan or Shaquille O'Neal?

5. George Blanda holds the NFL career scoring record (2002). Was he a quarterback or a placekicker?

6. In 1994, who broke Jim Brown's long-standing record of 126 career TD's—Marcus Allen or Jerry Rice?

7. True or false? Fran Tarkenton was a women's tennis champion.

8. Which swimmer holds the record for most national titles—Tracy Caulkins or Johnny Weissmuller?

9. Has anyone ever won all four of golf's Grand Slam titles in a single year?

10. Only one hockey player holds the career and season records for goals and assists. Who is it? (GEO-HINT: He's Great!)

11. Only one man has won tennis' Grand Slam twice. Was it Rod Laver or Bjorn Borg?

Top Trivia

▶ During a doubleheader in 1976, Texas Rangers shortstop Toby Harrah set a record for doing nothing—no fielding, no assists, no putouts. The ball never came his way. (Some record!)

▶ Mike Whalin of Ohio holds the record for bowling the most perfect games—48 of them. (Three strikes and you're . . . on your way!)

▶ Miguel Induráin's nickname is The Extraterrestrial, and his ability to win is "out of this world." Induráin is the first person ever to win five Tour de France bicycle races in a row.

Answers

1. False—Baltimore Oriole shortstop Cal Ripken, Jr. broke Gehrig's record of 2,130 games on September 6, 1995.

2. Pete Rose—With 4,265 hits in 11,429 at bats. (Although many consider Babe Ruth to be the greatest baseball player ever, few of his records still stand.)

3. False—That record is held by Kareem Abdul Jabbar.

4. Michael Jordan

5. Both—Leading scorers are usually kickers, but Blanda played both positions. He also holds records for most seasons as a pro (26) and most games played (340).

6. Jerry Rice (And he's still going!)

7. False—He was an NFL quarterback. Tarkenton holds many records, including career yardage (47,003), career completions (3,686), and career TD's (342).

8. Tracy Caulkins—She's won 48. (The record for a man is 36, by Johnny Weissmuller, who also played Tarzan in the movies.)

9. No—But Jack Nicklaus has won more of these tournaments than any other golfer.

10. Wayne Gretzky (The Great Gretzky)

11. Rod Laver—In 1962 and 1969

AMAZING FACTS

Javier Sotomayor's record high jump of 8 feet 1/2 inches (2.5 meters) was a little higher than a volleyball net!

Deion Sanders was the first athlete to hit a major league homer and score an NFL touchdown in the same week. He was also the first player to star in a World Series and a Super Bowl.

The Cy Young Award, given every year to the best pitcher in each league, is named after Denton T. Young, who became "Cy" when someone said the outfield fence he was throwing at to warm up looked like a cyclone hit it.

Top Teams

Mind Benders

1. Which team has won the most World Series—the New York Yankees or the Saint Louis Cardinals?

2. The NBA record for a winning streak is held by the Los Angeles Lakers. Did they win 11, 22, or 33 games in a row?

3. True or false? In 1988, the Miami Heat basketball team had a cold start, losing their first 17 games.

4. Was the point total in the highest-scoring NBA basketball game 270, 370, or 470?

5. What was the point total in the lowest-scoring NBA game—37 or 73?

6. Which team has won the most Super Bowl championships—the San Francisco 49ers or the Dallas Cowboys?

7. Was it Vince Lombardi or Don Shula who took the most teams to the Super Bowl?

8. Is the record for the most goals in a hockey game 16, 21, or 29?

9. Name the hockey team that has the most Stanley Cup championships. (GEO-HINT: They're from Canada's largest city.)

10. Which country has won soccer's World Cup more times than any other country—Germany, Brazil, or the U.S.?

Geo-Challenge

See if you can "letter" in sports by naming what these initials stand for.

NBA, NHL, NFL, AFC, NFC, AL, NL, PGA, NCAA

(Answers on page 32.)

Top Trivia

▶ **The fastest eight hockey goals were scored in five minutes flat by Toronto against the New York Americans in 1938.**

▶ **It took the Giants 51 minutes to beat the Phillies 6-1 on September 28, 1919—the shortest baseball game ever!**

▶ **The 1991 women's soccer world championship was won by the U.S. Women's National Team—the only U.S. team ever to win a major international soccer tournament.**

Answers

1. The New York Yankees—They have played in 33 World Series, winning 22 of them. (The Cardinals are a distant second, winning 9 of the 15 World Series they have played in.)

2. 33—In their 1971–72 championship season

3. True—And that's a record. (Brrr!)

4. 370—After three overtimes the Detroit Pistons beat the Denver Nuggets 186–184 on December 13, 1983.

5. 37—The Fort Wayne Pistons defeated the Minneapolis Lakers 19–18 on November 22, 1950. (What a snoozer!)

6. Trick question—Both have won the Super Bowl a record three times.

7. Don Shula—He led the Colts in III and the Dolphins in VI, VII, VIII, XVII and XIX.

8. 21—And it has been done twice, by the Montreal Canadiens vs. the Toronto St. Patricks in 1920 and by the Edmonton Oilers vs. the Chicago Blackhawks in 1985.

9. The Montreal Canadiens—With a record 24 wins and a record streak of 5 in a row!

10. Brazil has won four times.

Extreme Sports
Only If You Dare!

Mind Benders

1. What does a skysurfer need—a parachute, skyboard, or video camera?

2. Is the world record high dive from a diving board about as high as a six-story or sixteen-story building?

3. This "new" thrill sport is a 1,500-year-old tradition among some South Pacific islanders. Is it snowboarding, hang gliding, or bungee jumping?

4. The record speed is 135 mph (216 kph)! What's the sport—blindfolded motocross, barefoot water-skiing, or avalanche surfing?

5. This extreme sport uses special skateboards that reach speeds of almost 80 mph (128 kph). Is it called street luge or sui-sliding?

6. True or false? The dangerous and challenging sport of walrus wrestling is popular in some Arctic communities.

7. Choose one. Does spelunking take place in space, caves, or oceans?

8. Is mountain biking an Olympic sport?

9. True or false? The marathon is the longest of all running races.

10. Triathalon is three sports in one—running, swimming, and . . . what?

GEO-TIP *What makes extreme sports extreme? Most are either extremely dangerous or extremely demanding.*

Answers

1. All three—Skysurfers need skyboards to "surf," parachutes to land safely, and partners who can videotape their routines for the judges to see. (Oh yeah, they also need an airplane!)

2. A sixteen-story building—The record is 176 feet, 10 inches, or about 53.6 meters. (Let's hope it wasn't a belly flop!)

3. Bungee jumping

4. Barefoot water-skiing (Talk about amazing feets!)

5. Street luge

6. False (Not yet!)

7. Caves—Spelunking is cave exploration.

8. Yes—Starting with the 1996 Summer Olympics

9. False—Marathons are just over 26 miles (41.6 kilometers). Ultra-marathons are longer, like The Western States 100 (as in miles).

10. Cycling (The first and best known triathalon is the Hawaii Ironman.)

AMAZING FACTS

Heli-skiers are ski fanatics who fly by helicopter to isolated ski mountains. They wear special devices that give out radio signals so they can be found in case of an avalanche!

Triathlete Dave Scott has won the Hawaii Ironman six times! Paula Newby-Fraser has won the women's event six times, too. Both are records!

Boardsailer Jeff Olson has invented a new thrill sport he calls windfishing—dragging a deep-sea lure behind his sailboard until something bites. His record catch was a 28-pound (12-kilogram) fish!

Where the Games Are Played

Geography and Sports

1. Indianapolis wasn't always the home of football's Colts. Where did the team play before—Baltimore, Philadelphia, or Washington?

2. True or false? Football's Kansas City Chiefs play their home games in Kansas.

3. Which of these states does NOT have three professional football teams—Florida, California, or Texas?

4. Choose one. Which city used to have professional baseball and football teams with the same name—Cincinnati, St. Louis, or Boston?

5. Can you name two cities that have two professional baseball teams?

6. The Los Angeles Dodgers moved to California in 1958. Was the original baseball team called the Bronx, Brooklyn, or Bayside Dodgers?

7. True or false? All NHL hockey teams play in cities where hockey is a popular outdoor sport.

8. The Colorado Rockies hockey team left Colorado in 1982 and took a new name. Does the team now play in Michigan, New Jersey, or Minnesota?

9. The Los Angeles Clippers used to play basketball in another city. Was it San Francisco, San Diego, or San Jose?

10. True or false? All NBA basketball teams play their home games in the U.S.

GEO-TIP *Keep a map handy! That way you'll be in the know when teams are on the go, or even when a new franchise is added.*

AMAZING FACTS

Since the New York Giants and Jets both play their home games at the Meadowlands in New Jersey, one team has to move all of its equipment into the visiting team's locker room when they play each other.

When hockey's Minnesota North Stars moved *south* to Texas, they became the Dallas Stars.

When teams move, their names don't always travel well. Basketball's Utah Jazz used to be from New Orleans, the "jazz capital of the world," and the Los Angeles Lakers once played in Minneapolis, Minnesota, the "land of 10,000 lakes."

Answers

1. Baltimore

2. False—They play in Kansas City, Missouri.

3. Texas—The Jacksonville Jaguars, Miami Dolphins, and Tampa Bay Buccaneers play in Florida. The Oakland Raiders, San Diego Chargers, and San Francisco 49ers play in California. (Only the Houston Oilers and Dallas Cowboys play in Texas.)

4. St. Louis, Missouri—Both teams were called the Cardinals. The football team moved to Phoenix, 1988. Now they're the Arizona Cardinals.

5. Chicago (Cubs and White Sox) and New York (Mets and Yankees)

6. The Brooklyn Dodgers

7. False—Just try making ice outdoors if you're rooting for the Anaheim Mighty Ducks, Dallas Stars, Florida Panthers, L.A. Kings, San Jose Sharks, or Tampa Bay Lightning.

8. New Jersey—And now they're called the New Jersey Devils. Colorado has a new hockey team called the Avalanche.

9. San Diego—From 1978 to 1984

10. False—The NBA's Toronto Raptors and Vancouver Grizzlies play their home games in *Canada*.

THE END...

Geo-Challenge Answers

The Final Score

The Olympics (Page 8)	The Winter Olympics in 1998 will be held in Nagano, Japan, and the Summer Olympics in 2000 will be held in Sydney, Australia.

Superstars

(Page 10)

1.	E	4.	B	7.	H
2.	F	5.	C	8.	G
3.	A	6.	D		

Uniforms & Equipment

(Page 19)

pool ball

cricket ball

volleyball

bowling ball

handball

Team Trivia

(Page 20)

1.	B	3.	E	5.	A
2.	D	4.	G		

Record Breakers Overtime

(Page 26)

NBA	National Basketball Association	AFC	American Football Conference	NL	National League
NHL	National Hockey League	NFC	National Football Conference	PGA	Professional Golfers' Association
NFL	National Football League	AL	American League	NCAA	National Collegiate Athletics Association